What Can I Do?

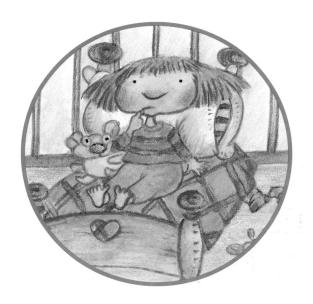

Written by Katherine Gillam
Illustrated by Esther Szedegy

Scott Foresman

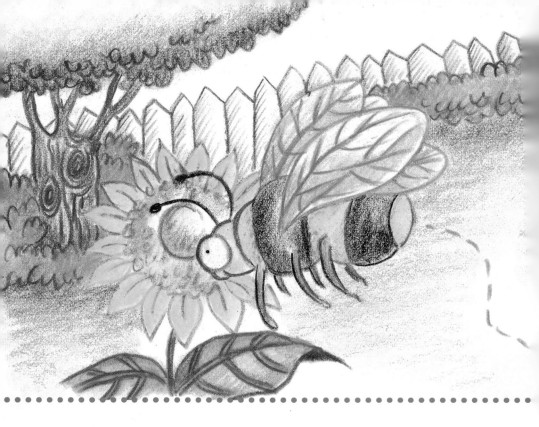

 A bee can buzz.

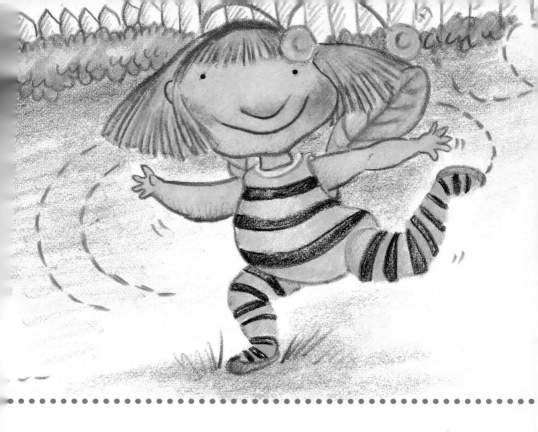

But so can I.

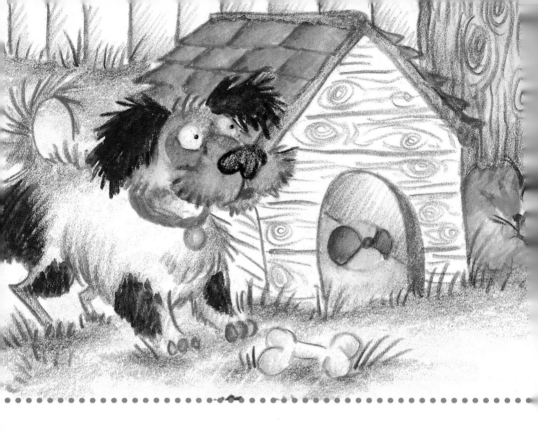

 A dog can bark.

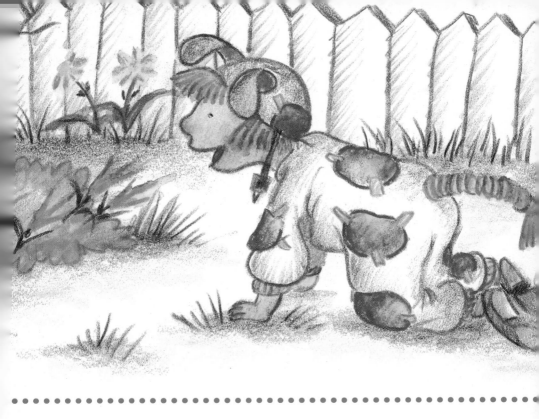

But so can I.

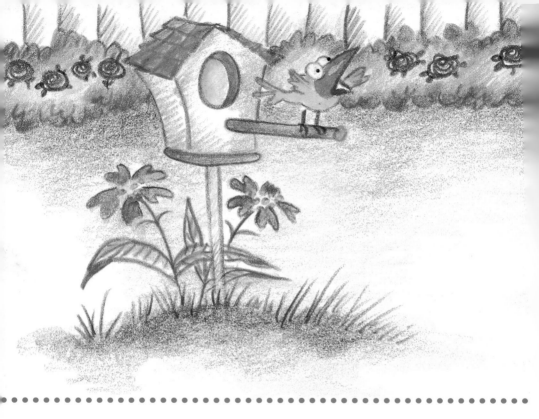

 A bird can sing.

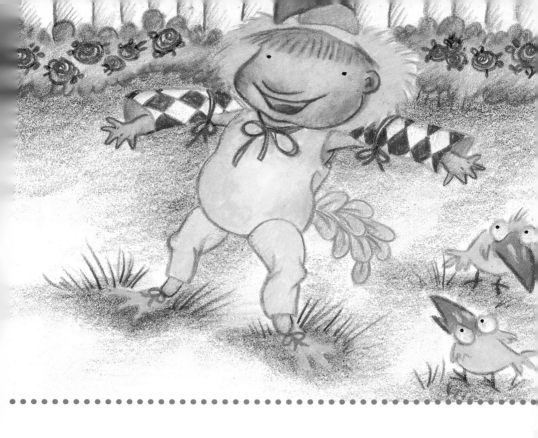

But so can I.

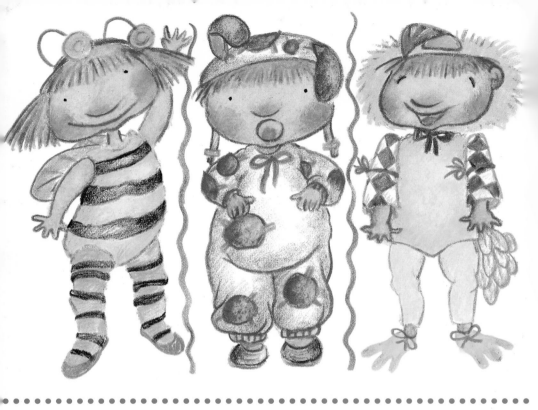

I can do all three!